MANIC STREET PREACHERS
EVERYTHING MUST GO
( )

SONY MUSIC PUBLISHING

EXCLUSIVE DISTRIBUTORS:

MUSIC SALES LIMITED
8/9 FRITH STREET, LONDON W1V 5TZ, ENGLAND.

MUSIC SALES PTY LIMITED
120 ROTHSCHILD AVENUE ROSEBERY, NSW 2018,
AUSTRALIA.

ORDER NO. AM939466
ISBN 0-7119-6015-1

VISIT THE INTERNET MUSIC SHOP AT
http://www.musicsales.co.uk

MUSIC ARRANGED AND PROCESSED BY
BARNES MUSIC ENGRAVING.

BOOK DESIGN BY MICHAEL BELL DESIGN.

PRINTED IN THE UNITED KINGDOM BY
PAGE BROS. LIMITED, NORWICH, NORFOLK.

THE PICTURES I CONTEMPLATE PAINTING WOULD CONSTITUTE A HALFWAY STATE AND AN ATTEMPT TO POINT OUT THE DIRECTION OF THE FUTURE - WITHOUT ARRIVING THERE COMPLETELY.

JACKSON POLLOCK

YOUR GUARANTEE OF QUALITY:

AS PUBLISHERS, WE STRIVE TO PRODUCE EVERY
BOOK TO THE HIGHEST COMMERCIAL STANDARDS.

THE MUSIC HAS BEEN FRESHLY ENGRAVED AND,
WHILST ENDEAVOURING TO RETAIN THE
ORIGINAL RUNNING ORDER OF THE RECORDED
ALBUM, THE BOOK HAS BEEN CAREFULLY DESIGNED
TO MINIMISE AWKWARD PAGE TURNS AND TO MAKE
PLAYING FROM IT A REAL PLEASURE.

PARTICULAR CARE HAS BEEN GIVEN TO SPECIFYING
ACID-FREE, NEUTRAL-SIZED PAPER MADE FROM PULPS
WHICH HAVE NOT BEEN ELEMENTAL CHLORINE
BLEACHED. THIS PULP IS FROM FARMED
SUSTAINABLE FORESTS AND WAS PRODUCED WITH
SPECIAL REGARD FOR THE ENVIRONMENT.

THROUGHOUT, THE PRINTING AND BINDING HAVE
BEEN PLANNED TO ENSURE A STURDY, ATTRACTIVE
PUBLICATION WHICH SHOULD GIVE YEARS OF
ENJOYMENT.

IF YOUR COPY FAILS TO MEET OUR
HIGH STANDARDS, PLEASE INFORM US AND WE
WILL GLADLY REPLACE IT.

MUSIC SALES' COMPLETE CATALOGUE
DESCRIBES THOUSANDS OF TITLES AND IS AVAILABLE
IN FULL COLOUR SECTIONS BY SUBJECT, DIRECT FROM
MUSIC SALES LIMITED. PLEASE STATE YOUR AREAS
OF INTEREST AND SEND A CHEQUE/POSTAL ORDER
FOR £1.50 FOR POSTAGE TO:

MUSIC SALES LIMITED
NEWMARKET ROAD, BURY ST. EDMUNDS,
SUFFOLK IP33 3YB.

NOTATION & TABLATURE EXPLAINED

Open C chord

Scale of E major

High E (1st) string
B (2nd) string
G (3rd) string
D (4th) string
A (5th) string
Low E (6th) string

Bent Notes

The note fretted is always shown first. Variations in pitch achieved by string bending are enclosed within this symbol ⌐ ¬. If you aren't sure how far to bend the string, playing the notes indicated without bending gives a guide to the pitches to aim for. The following examples cover the most common string bending techniques:

Example 1
Play the D, bend up one tone (two half-steps) to E.

Example 4
Pre-bend: fret the D, bend up one tone to E, then pick.

Example 2
Play the D, bend up one tone to E then release bend to sound D. Only the first note is picked.

Example 5
Play the A and D together, then bend the B-string up one tone to sound B.

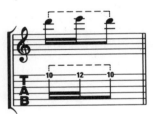

Example 3
Fast bend: Play the D, then bend up one tone to E as quickly as possible.

Example 6
Play the D and F# together, then bend the G-string up one tone to E, and the B-string up a semitone to G.

Additional guitaristic techniques have been notated as follows:

Tremolo Bar
Alter pitch using tremolo bar. Where possible, the pitch to aim for is shown.
a) Play the G; use the bar to drop the pitch to E.
b) Play the open G; use the bar to 'divebomb', i.e. drop the pitch as far as possible.

Mutes
a) Right hand mute
Mute strings by resting the right hand on the strings just above the bridge.
b) Left hand mute
Damp the strings by releasing left hand pressure just after the notes sound.
c) Unpitched mute
Damp the strings with the left hand to produce a percussive sound.

Hammer on and Pull off
Play first note, sound next note by 'hammering on', the next by 'pulling off'. Only the first note is picked.

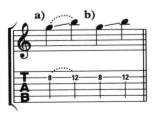

Glissando
a) Play first note, sound next note by sliding up string. Only the first note is picked.
b) As above, but pick second note.

Natural Harmonics
Touch the string over the fret marked, and pick to produce a bell-like tone. The small notes show the resultant pitch, where necessary.

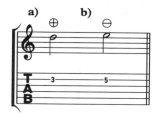

Slide Guitar
a) Play using slide.
b) Play without slide.

Artificial Harmonics
Fret the lowest note, touch string over fret indicated by diamond notehead and pick. Small notes show the resultant pitch.

Vibrato
Apply vibrato, by 'shaking' note or with tremolo bar. As vibrato is so much a matter of personal taste and technique, it is indicated only where essential.

Pinch Harmonics
Fret the note as usual, but 'pinch' or 'squeeze' the string with the picking hand to produce a harmonic overtone. Small notes show the resultant pitch.

Pick Scratch
Scrape the pick down the strings – this works best on the wound strings.

Microtones
A downwards arrow means the written pitch is lowered by less than a semitone; an upwards arrow raises the written pitch.

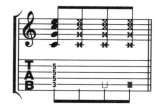

Repeated Chords
To make rhythm guitar parts easier to read the tablature numbers may be omitted when a chord is repeated. The example shows a C major chord played naturally, r/h muted, l/h muted and as an unpitched mute respectively.

Special Tunings
Non-standard tunings are shown as 'tuning boxes'. Each box represents one guitar string, the leftmost box corresponding to the lowest pitched string. The symbol '•' in a box means the pitch of the corresponding string is not altered. A note within a box means the string must be re-tuned as stated. For tablature readers, numbers appear in the boxes. The numbers represent the number of half-steps the string must be tuned up or down. The tablature relates to an instrument tuned as stated.

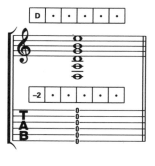

Tune the low E (6th) string down one tone (two half-steps) to D.

Chord naming
The following chord naming convention has been used:

C   Cm   C5   Csus4   Csus$\frac{4}{2}$ C(♭5)   Cdim   Caug   C6   Cm6   Cmaj7   C7   C7♯5   C7♭5   Cm7   Cm7♭5   Cdim7   Cmaj9   C9   Cm9   C7♭9   C7♯9   Cadd9   C/B♭

Where there is no appropriate chord box, for example when the music consists of a repeated figure (or riff) the tonal base is indicated in parenthesis: **[C]**

Where it was not possible to transcribe a passage, the symbol ∿ appears.

ELVIS IMPERSONATOR: BLACKPOOL PIER

MUSIC BY JAMES DEAN BRADFIELD & SEAN MOORE
LYRICS BY NICKY WIRE & RICHEY JAMES

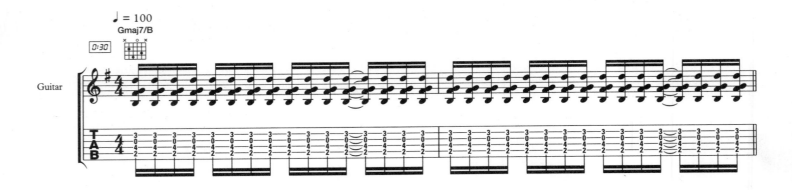

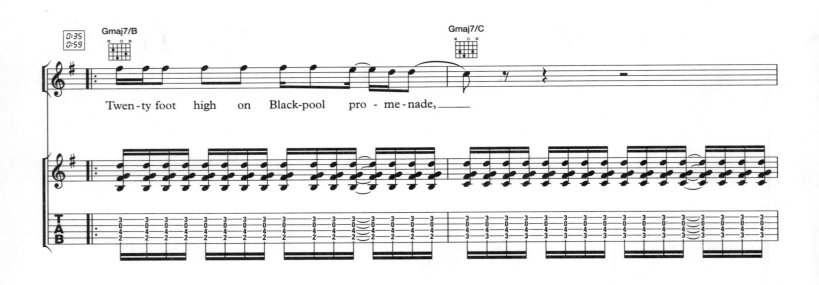

Twen-ty foot high on Black-pool pro - me-nade,

fake roy-al-ty se-cond hand se - quin fa - cade,

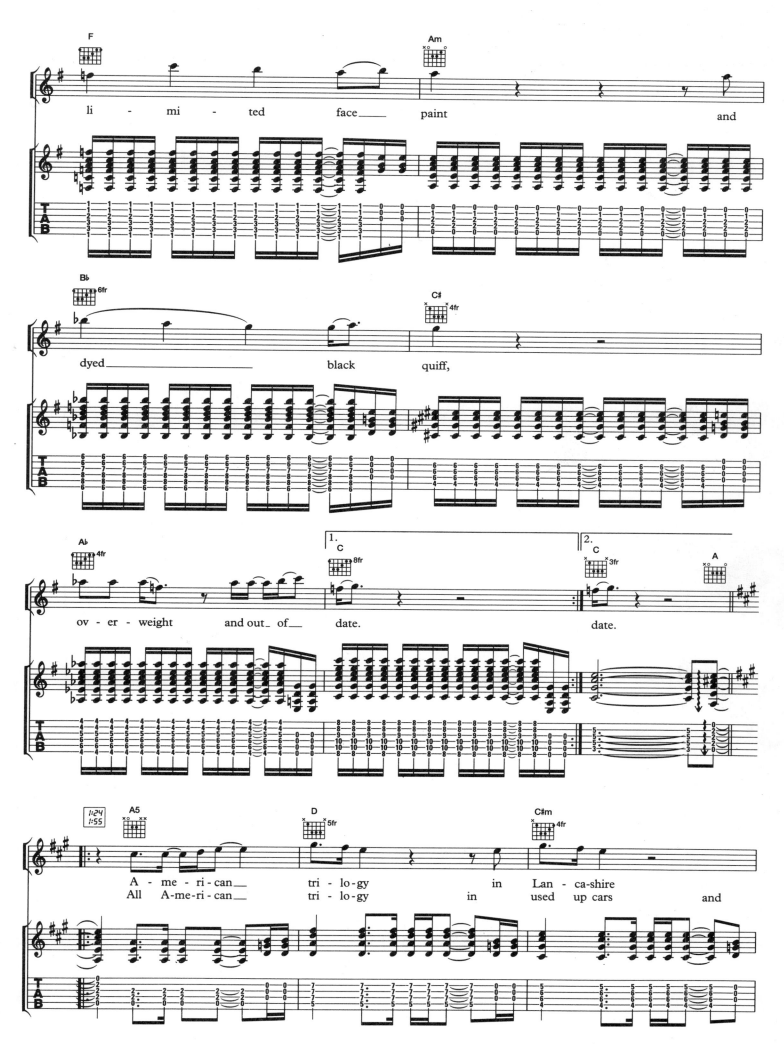

li - mi - ted face___ paint and

dyed _____ black quiff,

ov - er - weight and out_ of___ date. date.

A - me - ri - can___ tri - lo - gy in Lan - ca-shire
All A - me - ri - can___ tri - lo - gy in used up cars and

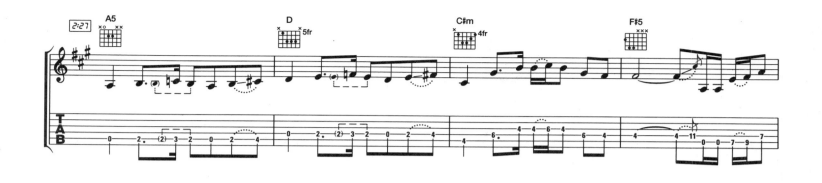

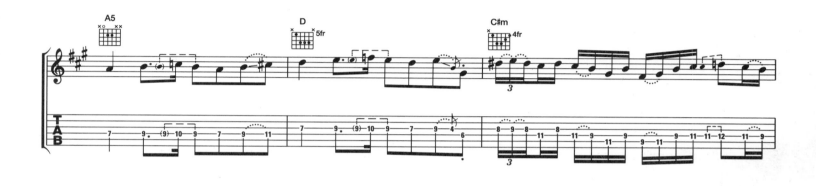

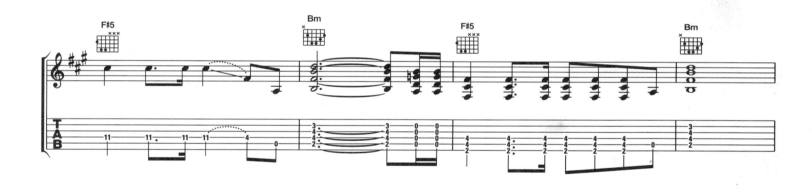

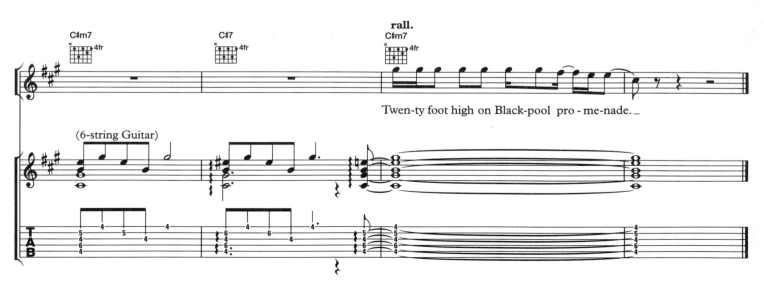

Twen-ty foot high on Black-pool pro - me-nade.

(6-string Guitar)

A DESIGN FOR LIFE

MUSIC BY JAMES DEAN BRADFIELD & SEAN MOORE
LYRICS BY NICKY WIRE

13

KEVIN CARTER

MUSIC BY JAMES DEAN BRADFIELD, SEAN MOORE & NICKY WIRE
LYRICS BY RICHEY JAMES

Hi_____ Time ma - ga - zine,   hi Pu - lit - zer_____ prize,
Hi_____ Time ma - ga - zine,   hi Pu - lit - zer_____ prize,

tri - bal___ scars   in___ tech - ni - col   - our,___
vul - ture stalked   white_ piped lie   for - ev - er,___

Dear Julia

Their is nothing I can say or do that will change what has been said between us but I do know that my feelings for you have not faltered and are Just as strong. I am feeling very upset and empty inside and very lonley, maybe you understand and I Just do not see it. I dont blame you if your feelings for me have changed at all, I have not made it easy for myself to get along with. I have this insecurity which is playing on my mind far to often for my liking, it gets me down and I do not like that, believe it or not their is so much inside of me that people do not see, maybe if I let some of it out personality wise. I love it when I am happy with you I feel so bubbly. I could tell you time & time again that I love you, but those three words cannot really show you my feelings or describe them, like when I am away from you I have a physical pain in my heart and believe it or not, but i swear on my life its there and its feels like my heart is reaching out for you but your not here and then I feel empty inside, these words are true I swear to you.

Their are so many things to look forward too such as being together going on weekends away, italy and having our home, cycling, swimming going for walks, but with out you there all these things have no meaning. I dont want to be with out you I would be heart broken.

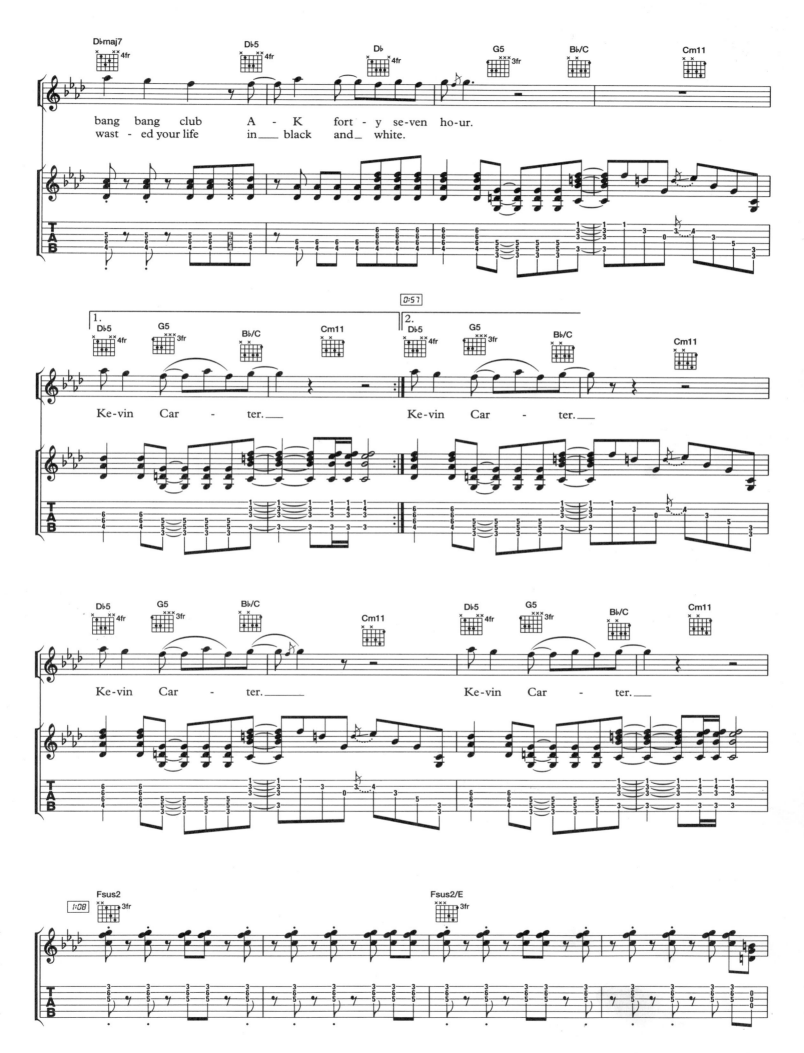

bang bang club   A - K   fort - y se-ven ho-ur.
wast - ed your life   in___ black   and___ white.

Ke-vin   Car   -   ter.___   Ke-vin   Car   -   ter.___

Ke-vin   Car   -   ter.___   Ke-vin   Car   -   ter.___

Mmm, wooh, ooh,_____ ooh, ooh, ooh,_____

Ke - vin Car - ter.____ The

el - e - phant is so___ ug - ly he sleeps his head, ma - che - tes his bed,___

Ke - vin___ Car - ter Kaf - fir lov - er for - ev - er.___

Click click click click click click___ him-self un - der.

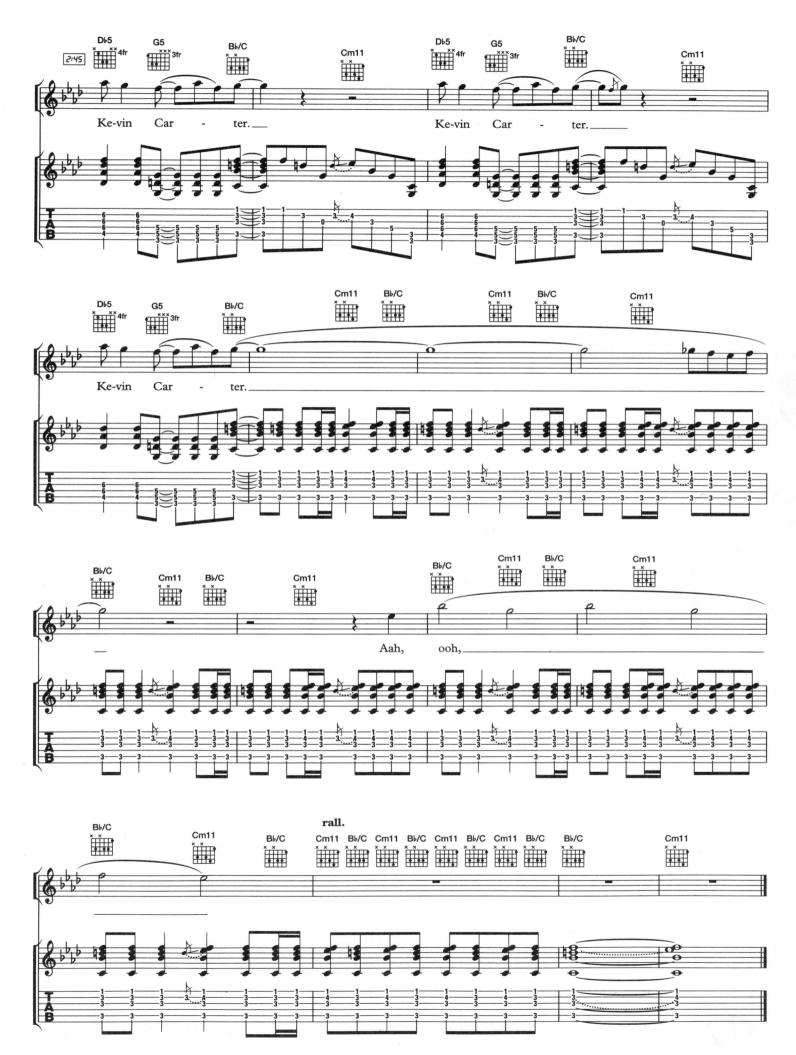

Ke-vin Car - ter. Ke-vin Car - ter.

Ke-vin Car - ter.

Aah, ooh,

rall.

ENOLA/ALONE

MUSIC BY JAMES DEAN BRADFIELD & SEAN MOORE
LYRICS BY NICKY WIRE

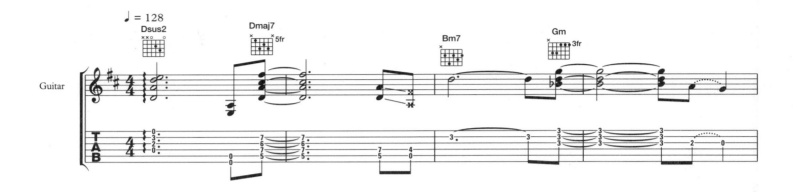

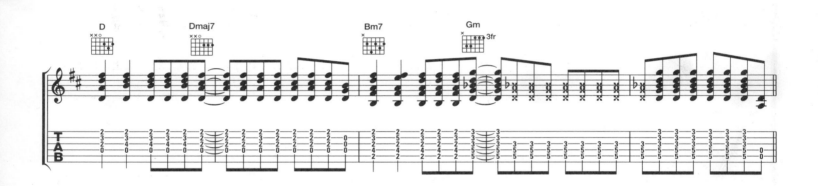

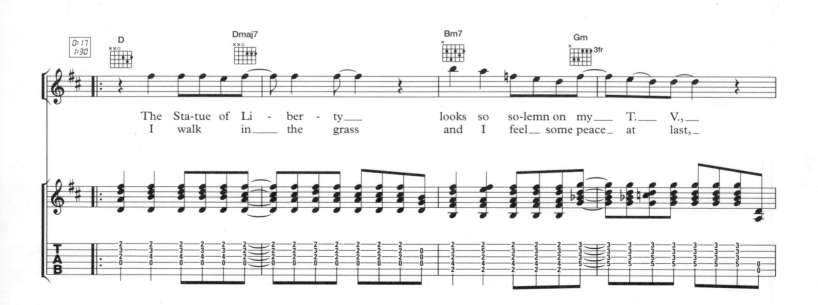

The Sta-tue of Li-ber-ty____ looks so so-lemn on my___ T.___ V.,___
I walk in___ the grass and I feel___ some peace___ at last,___

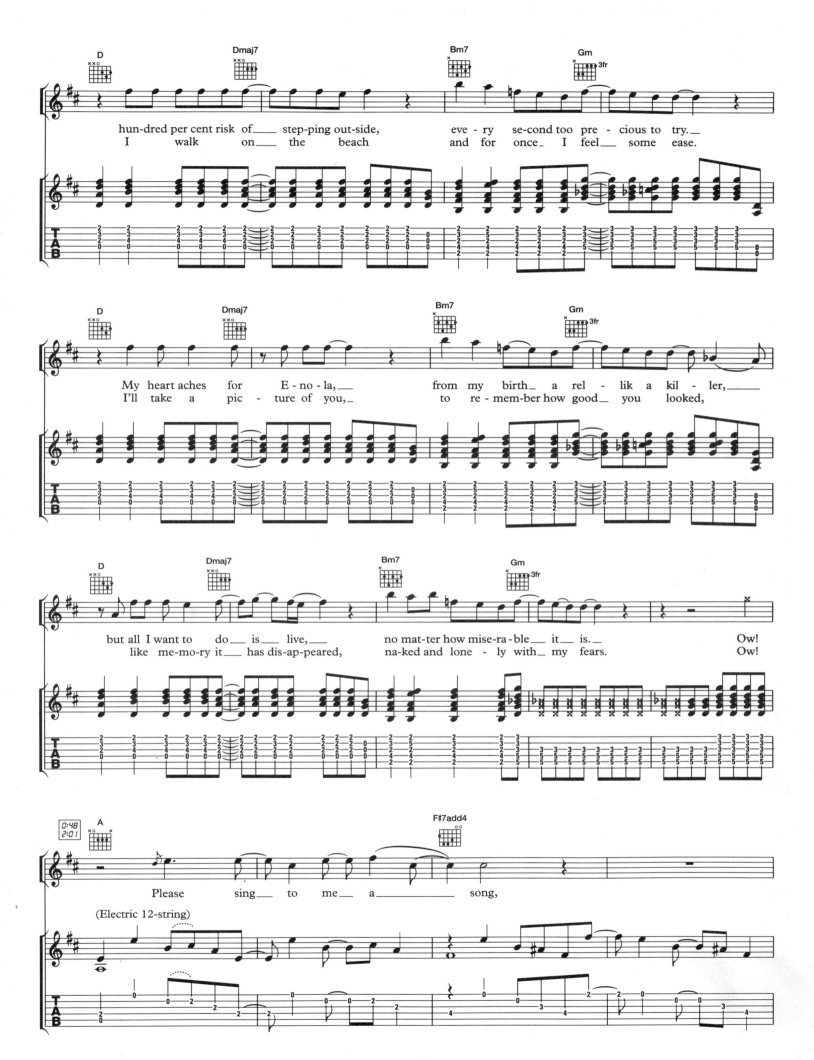

hun-dred per cent risk of___ step-ping out-side, eve - ry se-cond too pre - cious to try.___
I walk on___ the beach and for once_ I feel___ some ease.

My heart aches for E - no - la,___ from my birth_ a rel - lik a kil - ler,___
I'll take a pic - ture of you,_ to re - mem-ber how good_ you looked,

but all I want to do___ is___ live,___ no mat-ter how mise-ra-ble___ it___ is._ Ow!
like me-mo-ry it___ has dis-ap-peared, na-ked and lone - ly with_ my fears._ Ow!

Please sing___ to me a_____ song,

(Electric 12-string)

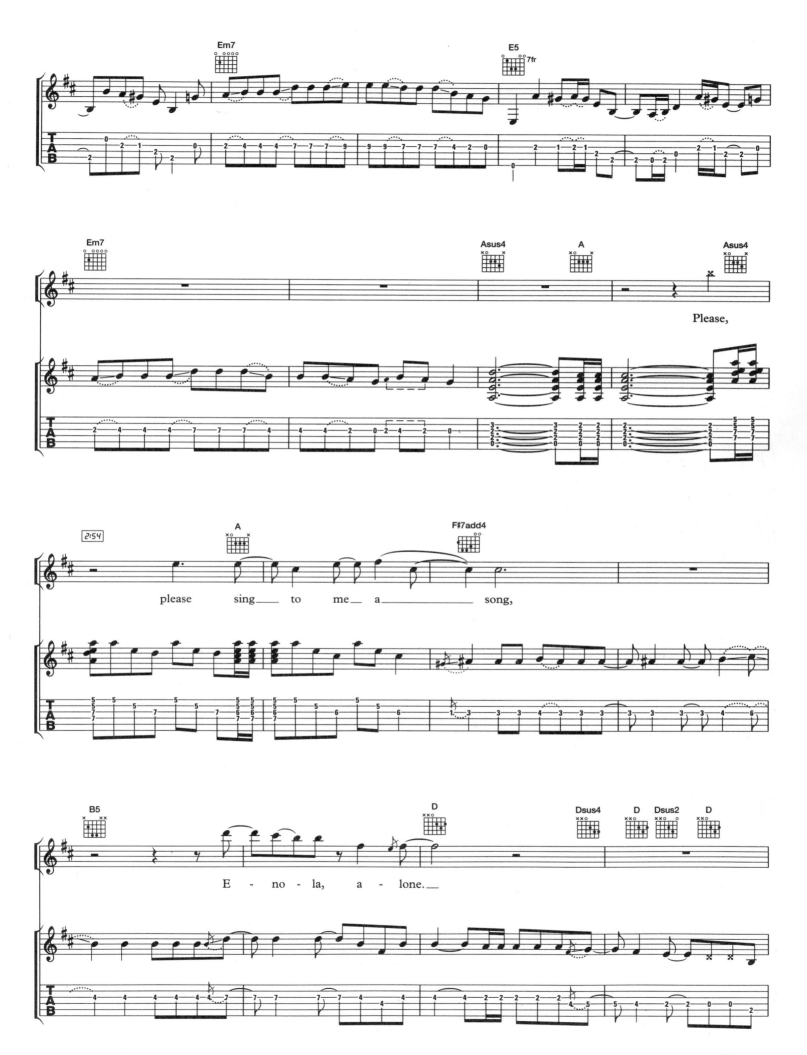

Please,
please sing___ to me a_____ song,
E - no - la, a - lone.___

THE GIRL WHO WANTED TO BE GOD

MUSIC BY JAMES DEAN BRADFIELD & SEAN MOORE
LYRICS BY NICKY WIRE & RICHEY JAMES

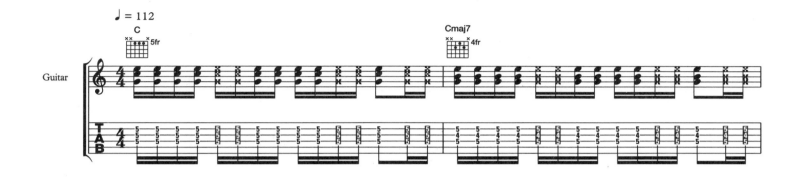

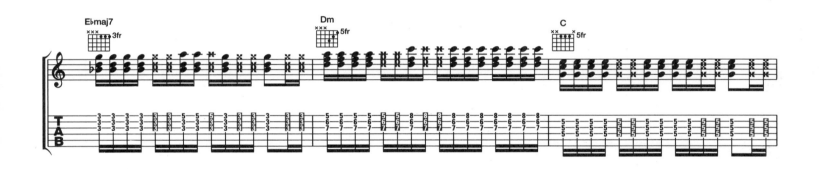

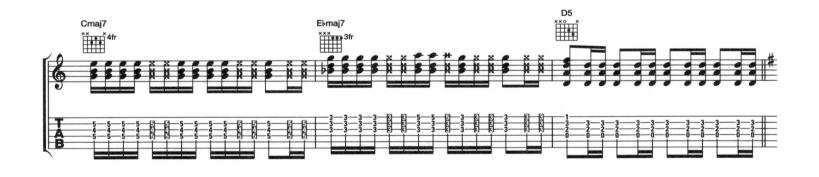

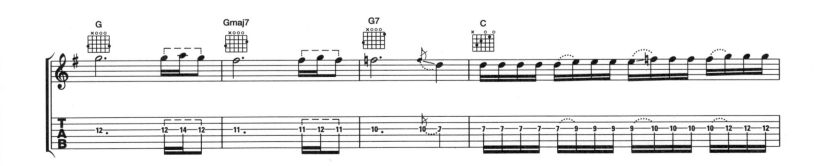

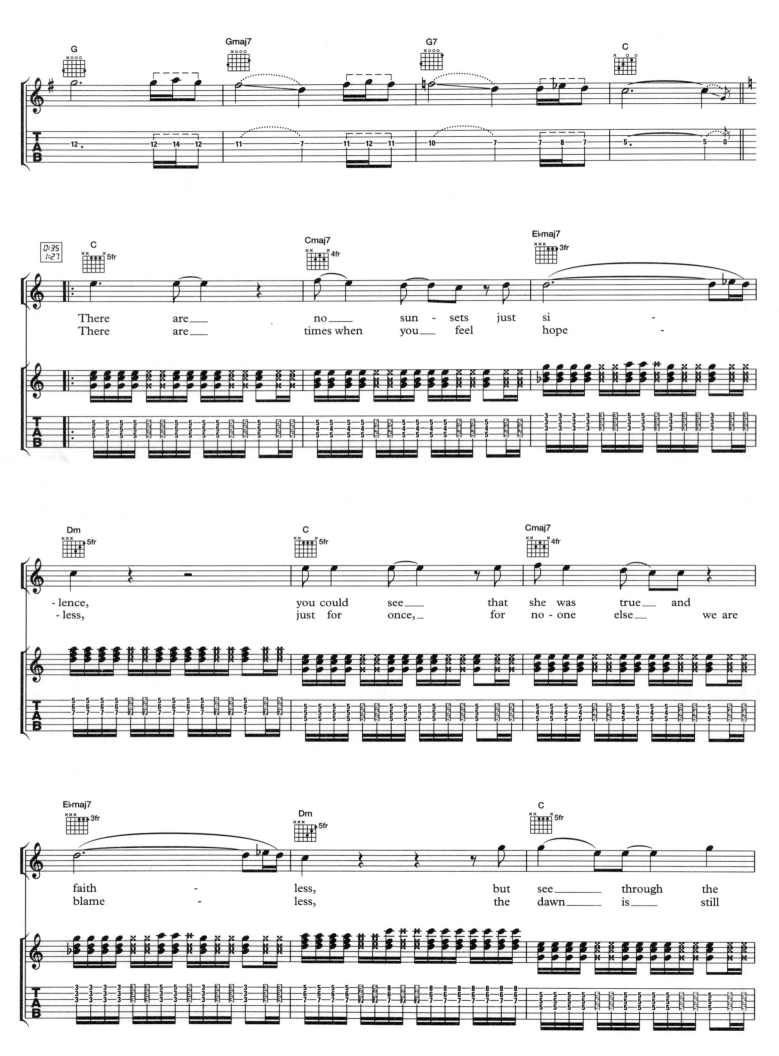

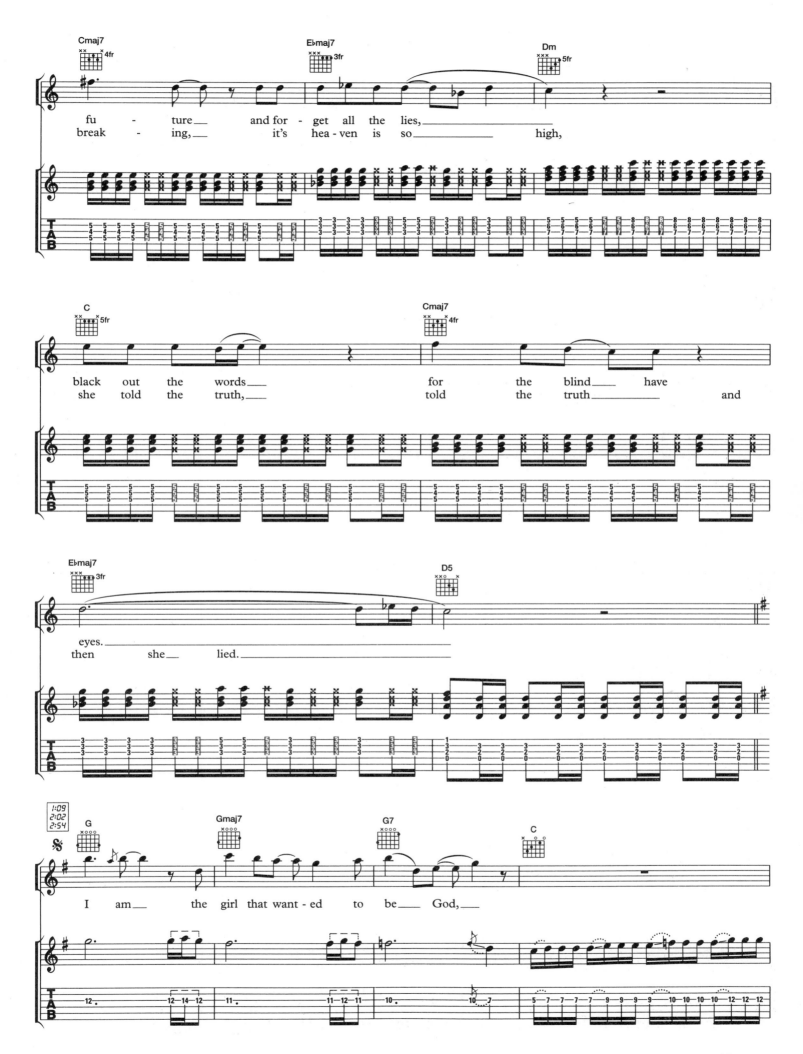

I am the girl that want - ed to be God.

Hold me she said, love me to

death.

EVERYTHING MUST GO

MUSIC BY JAMES DEAN BRADFIELD & SEAN MOORE
LYRICS BY NICKY WIRE

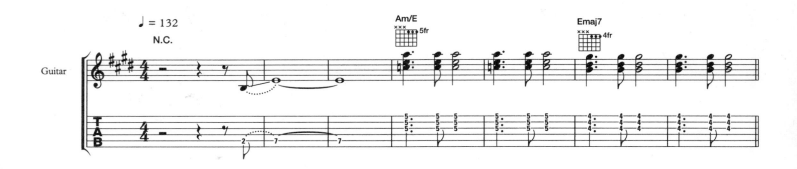

Shed some skin___ for the fear with - in, is start-ing to hurt
I look to the fu - ture it makes me cry, but it seems too_

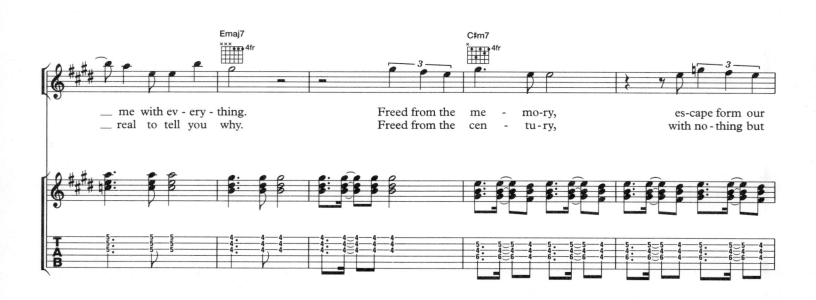

___ me with ev - ery - thing. Freed from the me - mo - ry, es-cape form our
___ real to tell you why. Freed from the cen - tu - ry, with no - thing but

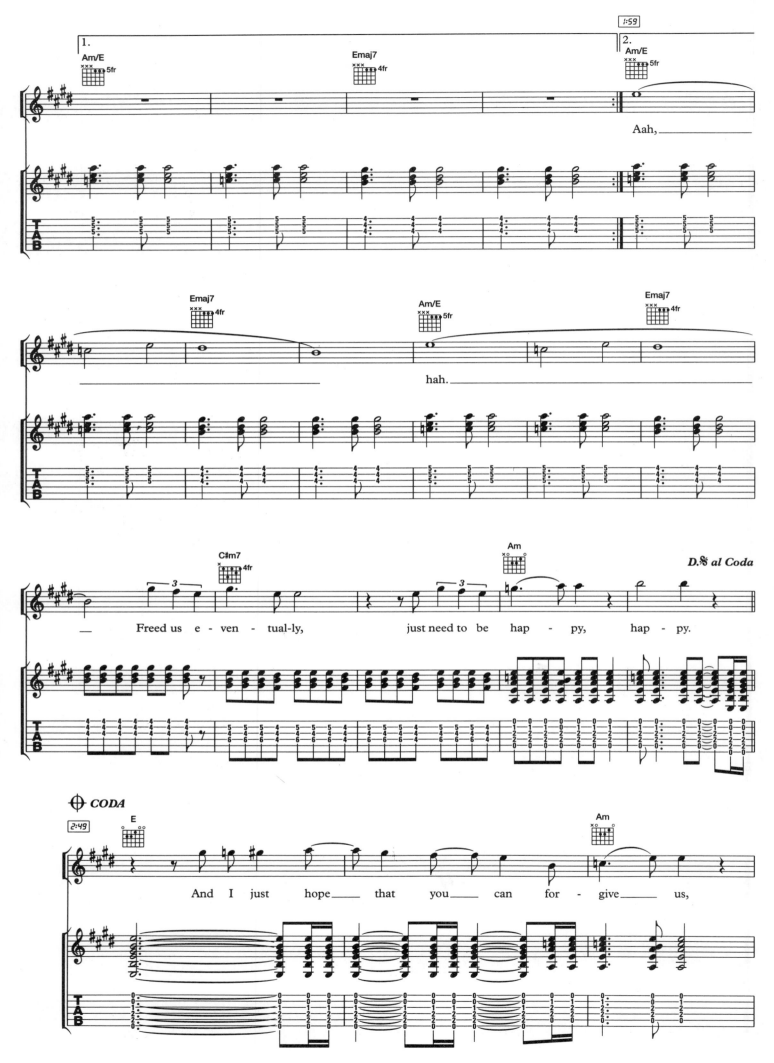

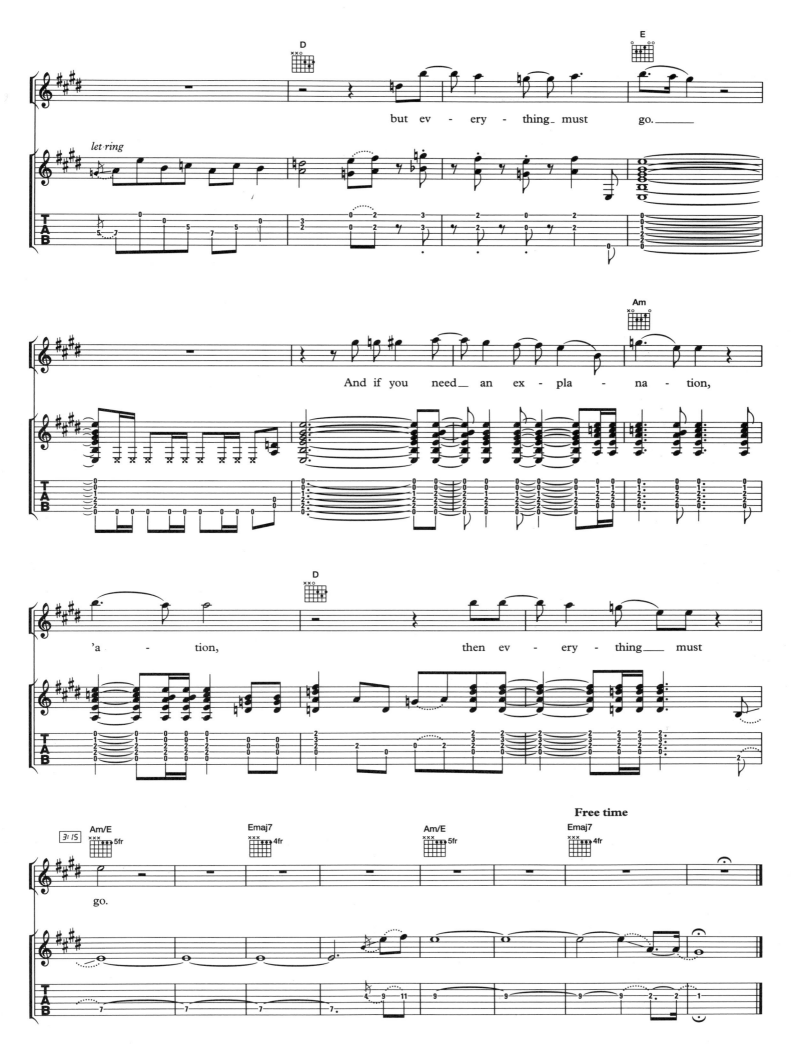

but ev - ery - thing_ must go. _____

And if you need_ an ex - pla - na - tion,

'a - tion, then ev - ery - thing_ must

go.

SMALL BLACK FLOWERS THAT GROW IN THE SKY

MUSIC BY JAMES DEAN BRADFIELD, SEAN MOORE & NICKY WIRE
LYRICS BY RICHEY JAMES

You have your ve - ry own num - ber,
They drag sticks a - long your walls, _____

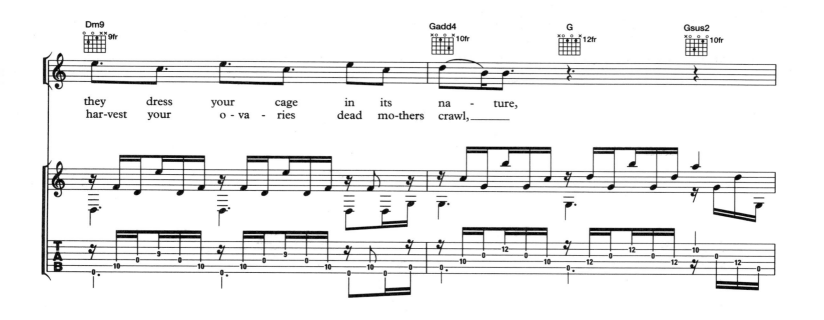

they dress your cage in its na - ture,
har-vest your o - va - ries dead mo-thers crawl,_____

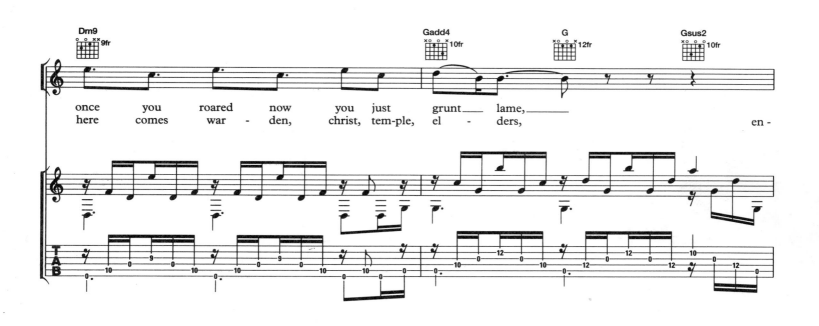

once you roared now you just grunt_____ lame,_____
here comes war - den, christ, tem-ple, el - ders,   en -

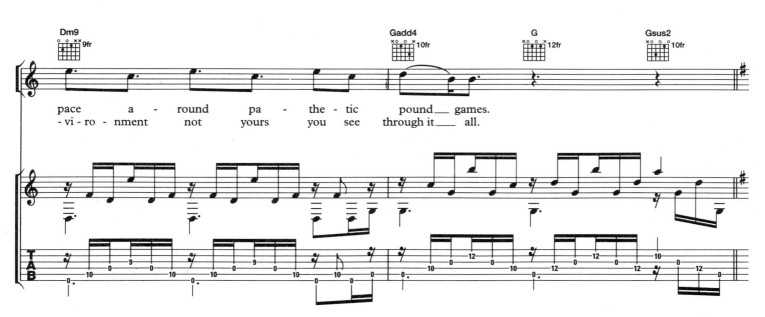

pace a - round pa - the - tic pound_____ games.
-vi - ro - nment not yours you see through it_____ all.

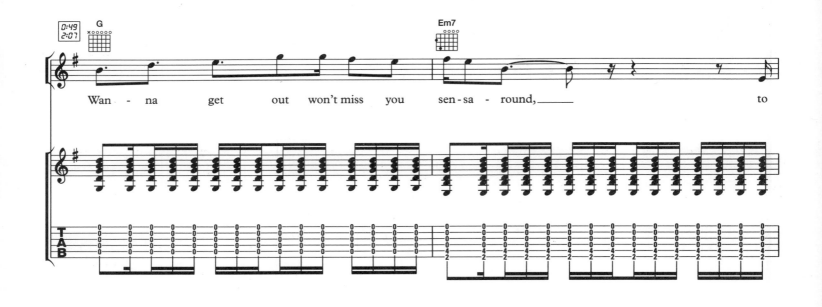

Wan - na get out won't miss you sen - sa - round,_____ to

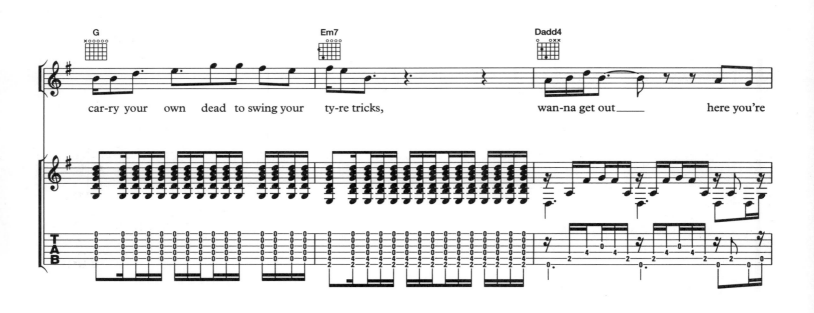

car-ry your own dead to swing your ty-re tricks, wan-na get out_____ here you're

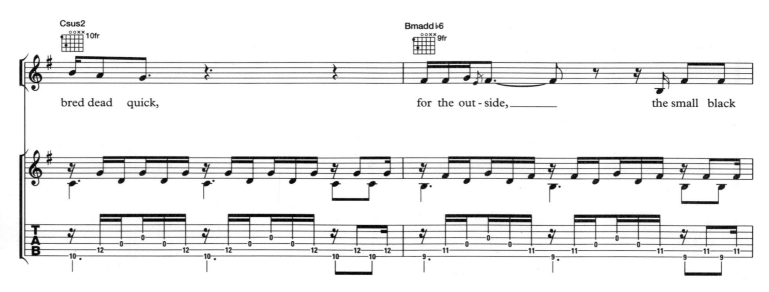

bred dead quick, for the out-side,_____ the small black

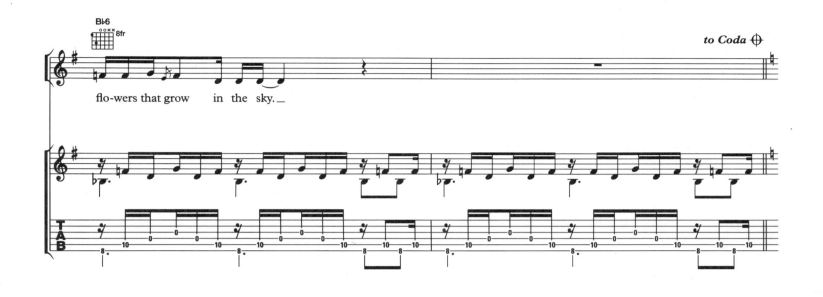

flo-wers that grow in the sky. __

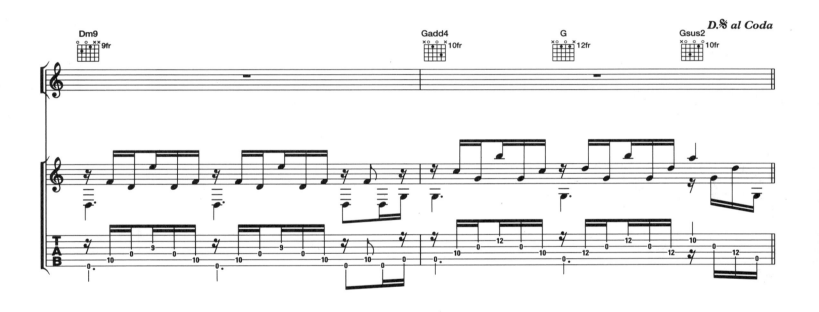

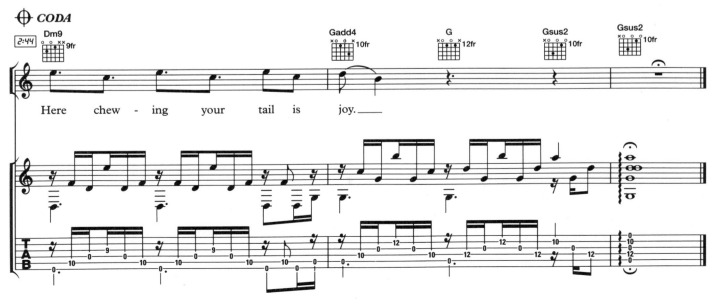

Here chew - ing your tail is joy. ____

REMOVABLES

MUSIC BY JAMES DEAN BRADFIELD, SEAN MOORE & NICKY WIRE
LYRICS BY RICHEY JAMES

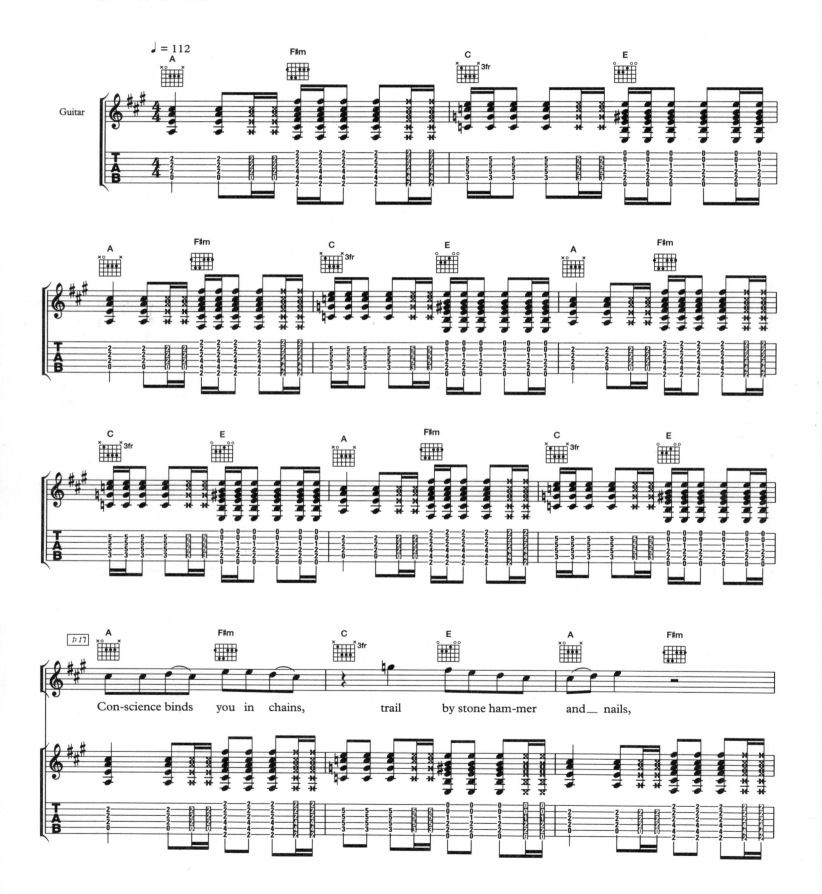

Con-science binds you in chains, trail by stone ham-mer and__ nails,

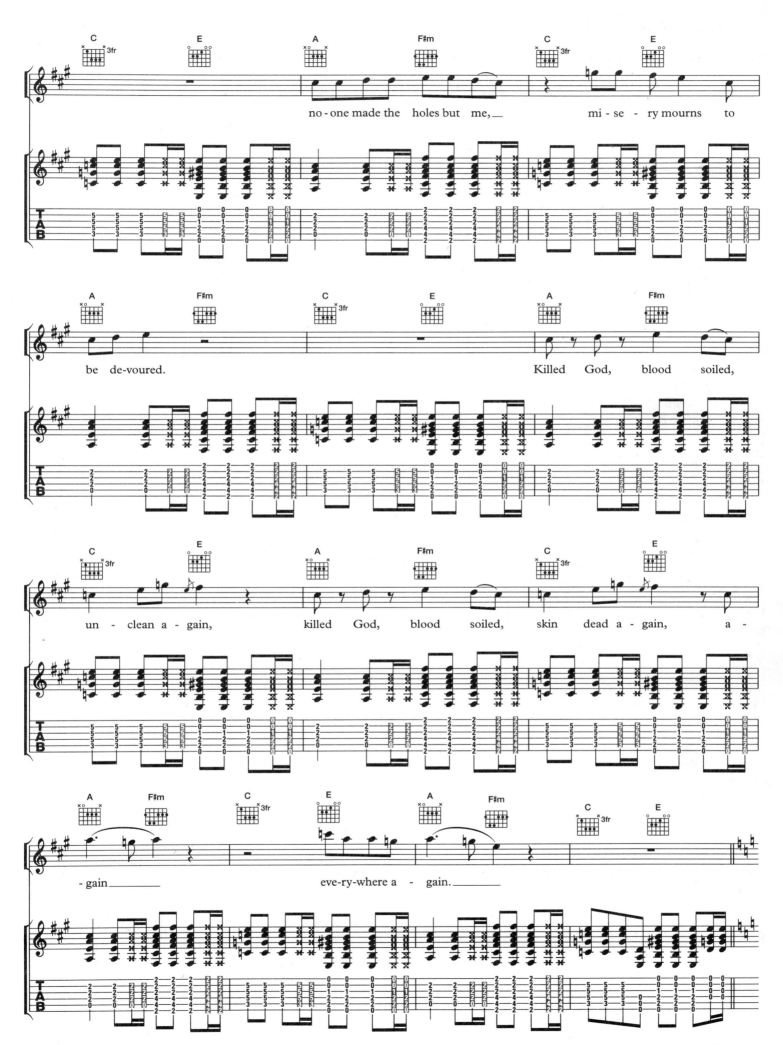

no - one made the holes but me, ___ mi - se - ry mourns to

be de-voured. Killed God, blood soiled,

un - clean a - gain, killed God, blood soiled, skin dead a - gain, a -

- gain ___ eve-ry-where a - gain. ___

All re - mov - a - bles, all tran - si - to - ry,_____

all re - mov - a - bles, pass - ing al - ways,_____

all re - mov - a - bles, all tran - si - to - ry,_____

all re - mov - a - bles, pass - ing al - ways._____

to Coda

Ne - ver grown pre - served gent - ly,____ a bronze moth dies____ ea - si - ly,

un - known to oth - ers weak to me,____ bro - ken hands ne - ver

end - ing. Aim-less rut of my____

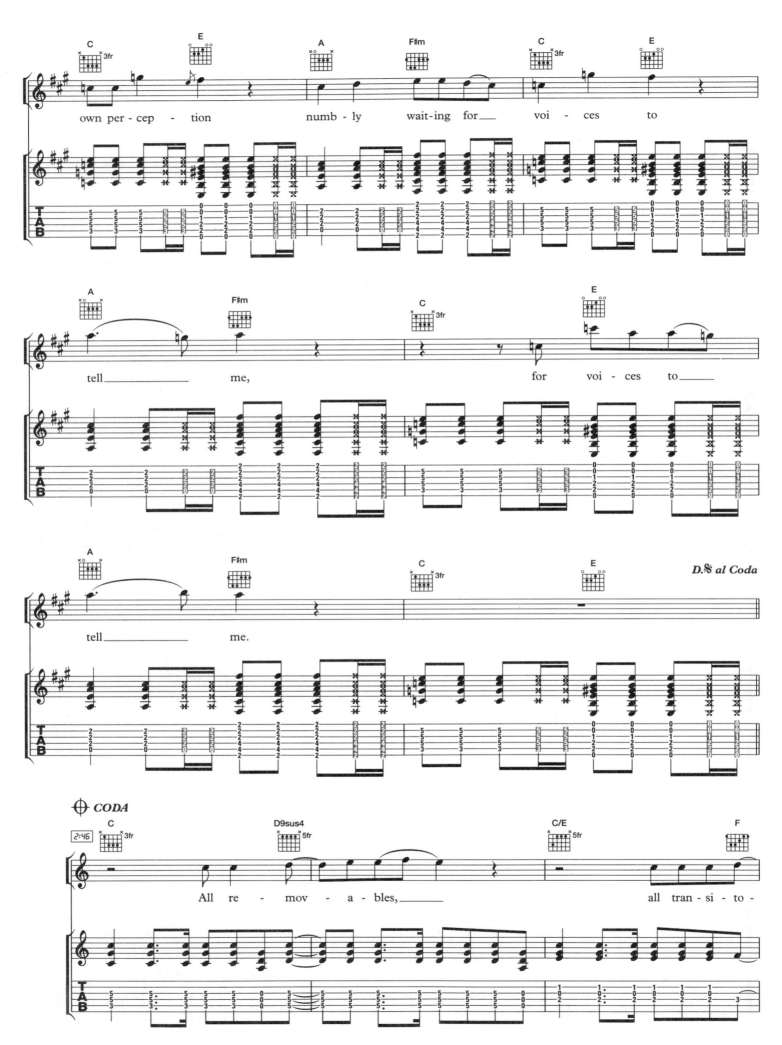

own per-cep - tion   numb-ly   wait-ing for___   voi - ces   to

tell_____   me,   for   voi - ces   to_____

tell_____   me.

D.%. al Coda

CODA

All re - mov - a - bles,_____   all tran - si - to -

42

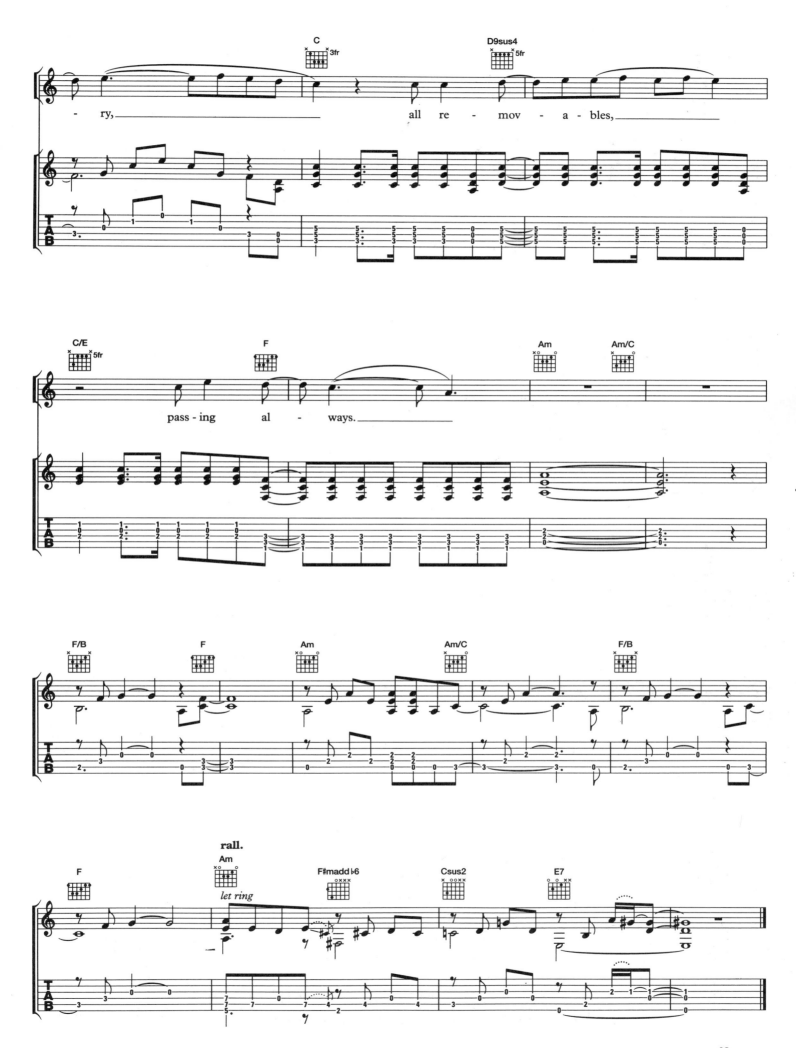

INTERIORS (SONG FOR WILLEM DE KOONING)

MUSIC BY JAMES DEAN BRADFIELD & SEAN MOORE
LYRICS BY NICKY WIRE

FURTHER AWAY

MUSIC BY JAMES DEAN BRADFIELD & SEAN MOORE
LYRICS BY NICKY WIRE

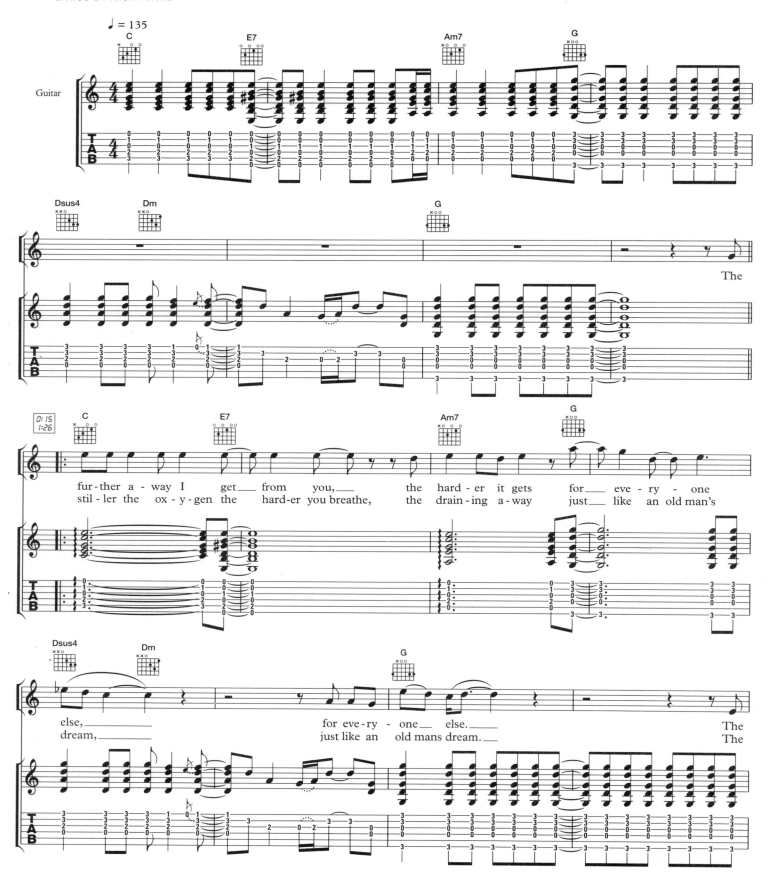

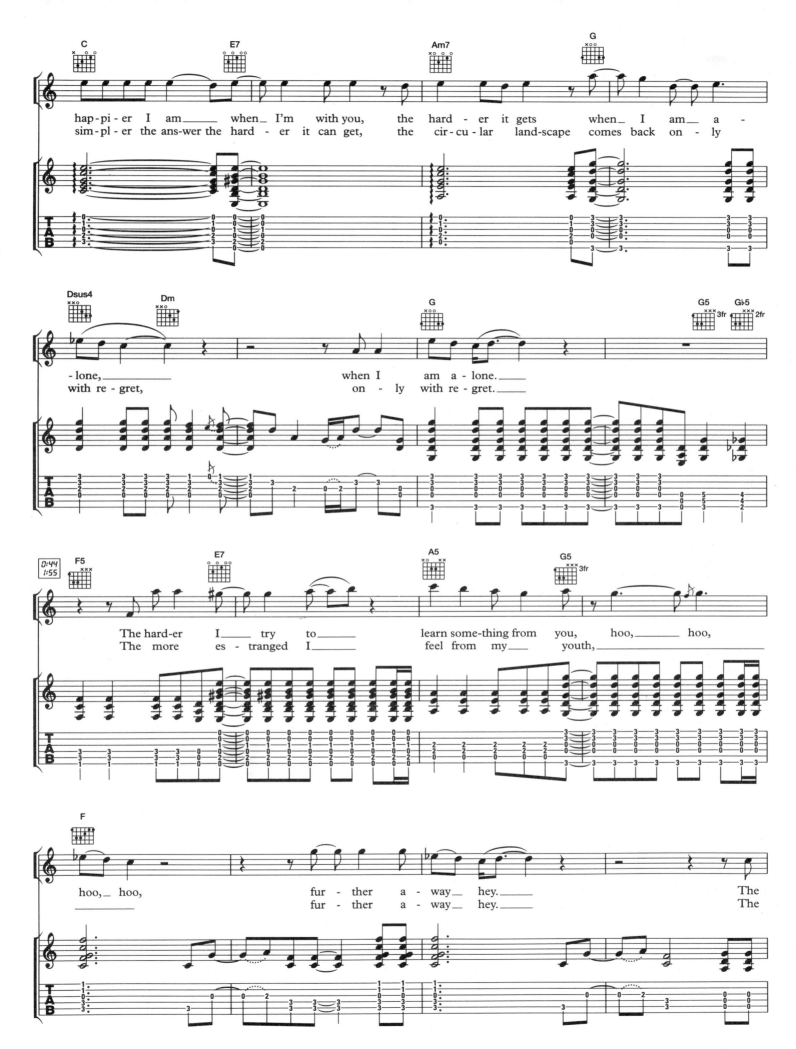

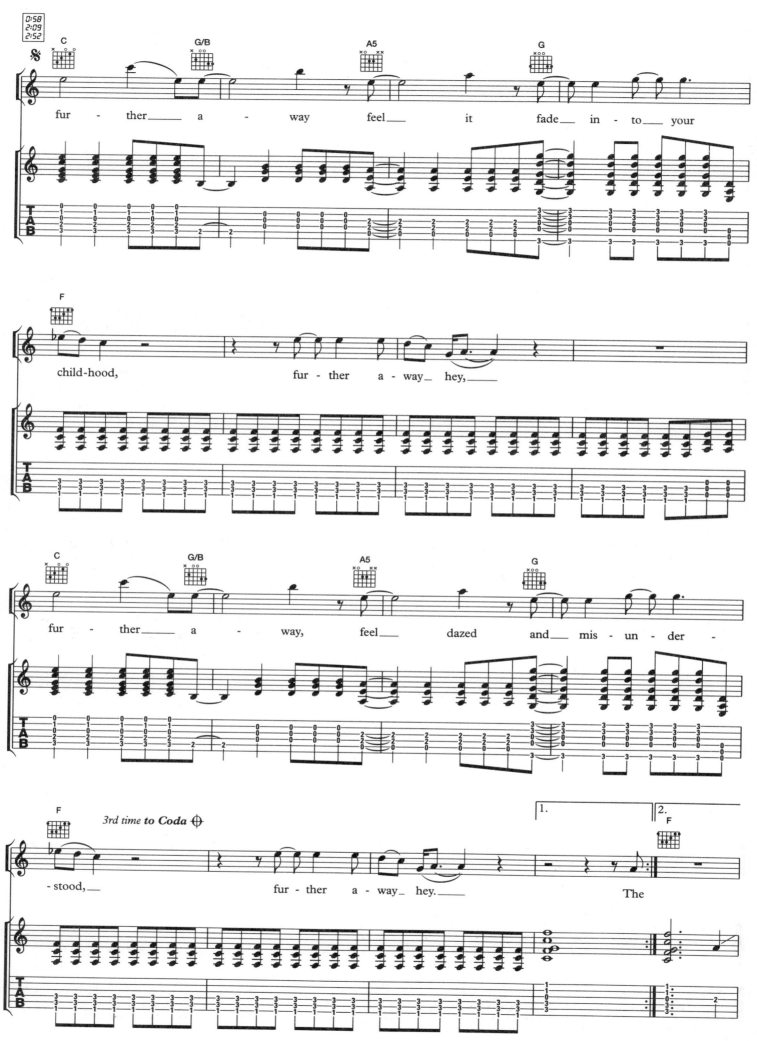

further____ a - way feel____ it fade____ in - to___ your

child-hood, fur - ther a - way__ hey,_____

fur - ther_____ a - way, feel____ dazed and____ mis - un - der -

3rd time to Coda

- stood,___ fur - ther a - way__ hey.____ The

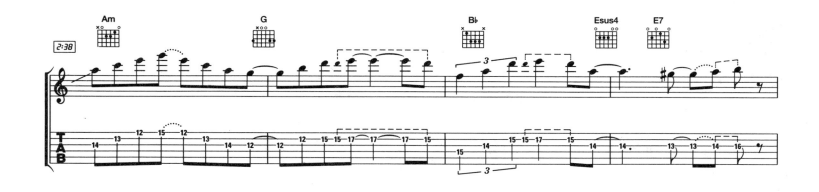

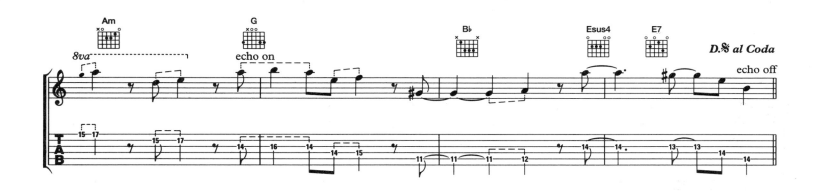

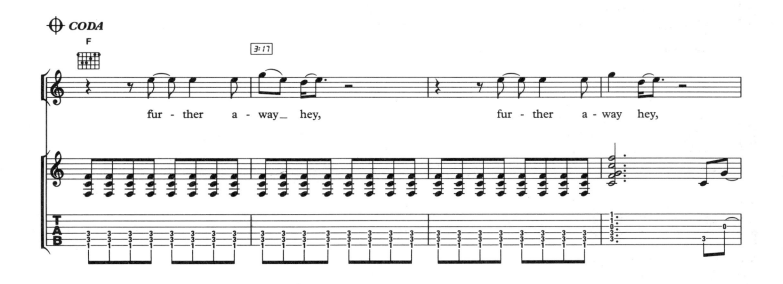

AUSTRALIA

MUSIC BY JAMES DEAN BRADFIELD & SEAN MOORE
LYRICS BY NICKY WIRE

it must be   for_ the ve - ry last___ time,   it's twelve_ o'-clock till

mid - night,   there_ must be some-one to   blame.

D.%̸ al Coda

⊕ *CODA*

- a.

[C]

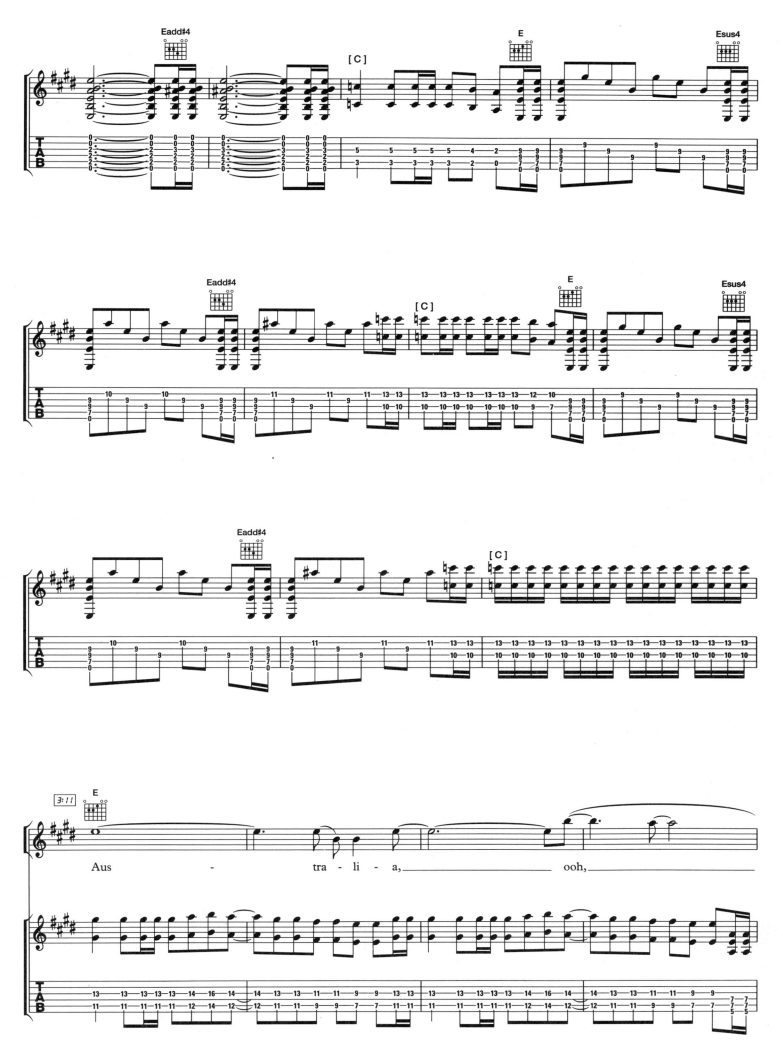

NO SURFACE ALL FEELING

MUSIC BY JAMES DEAN BRADFIELD & SEAN MOORE
LYRICS BY NICKY WIRE

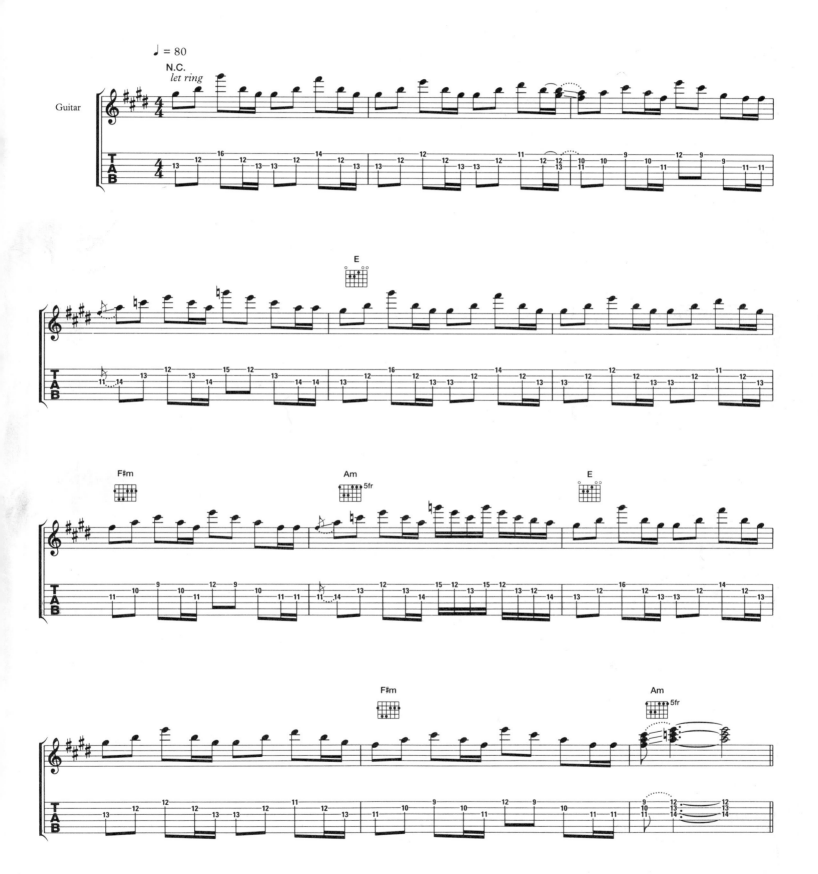

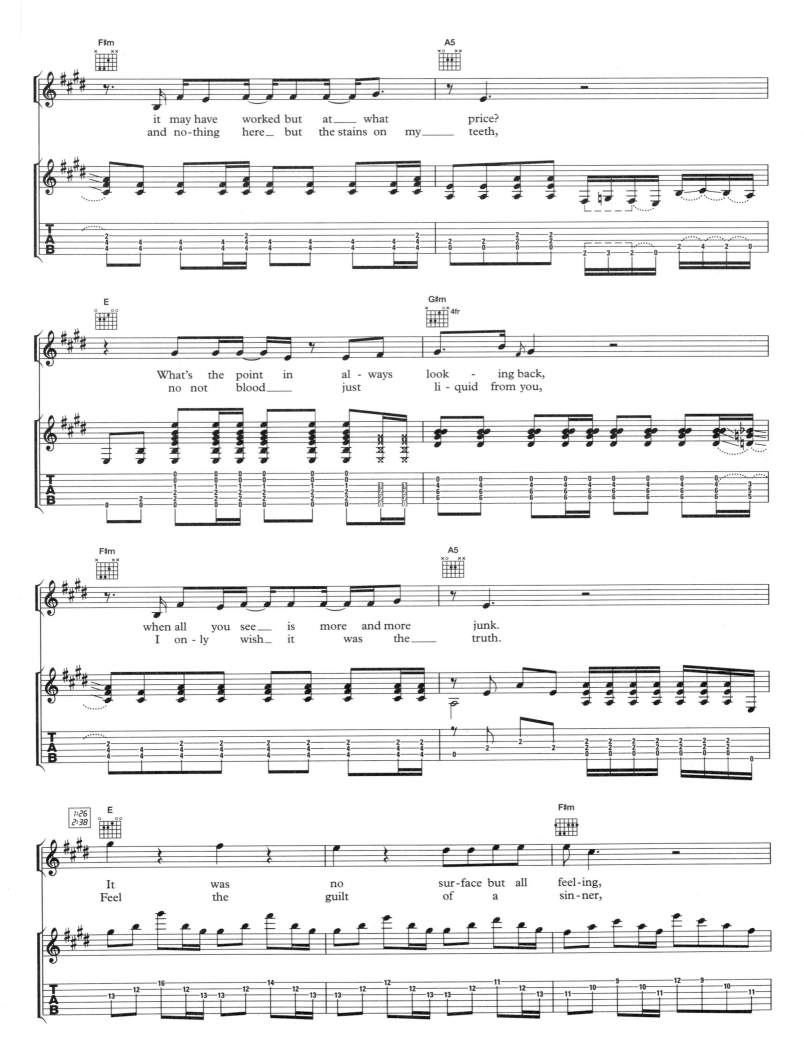

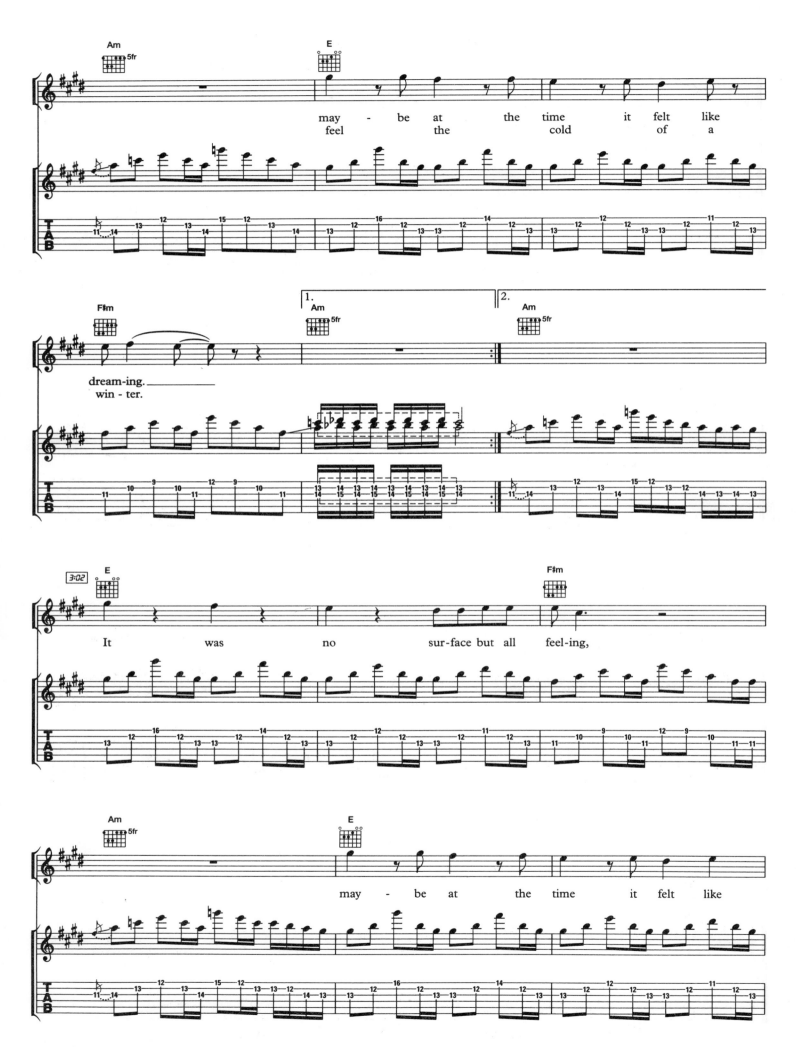

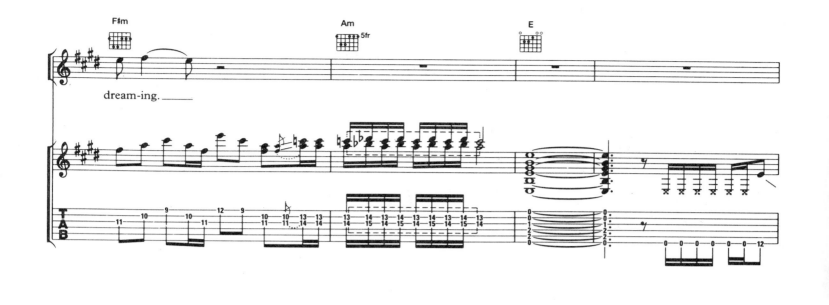

dream-ing. ____

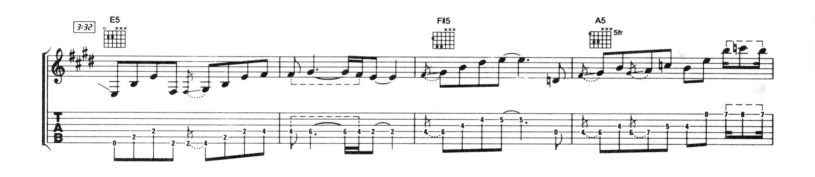

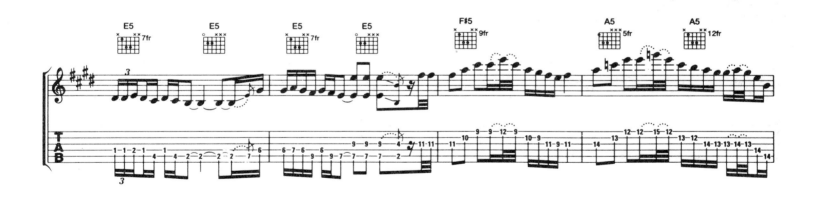

Free time